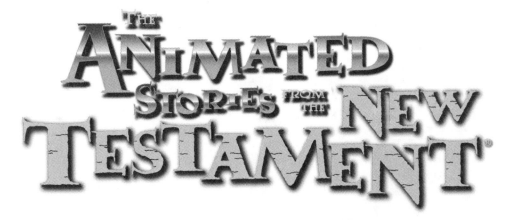

NEST Complete Learning System™

THE ANIMATED STORIES FROM THE NEW TESTAMENT®

Resource & Activity Book

The Lord's Prayer

By: Terry Noss, Timothy Yoo, Bronwen Barry,
Elena Kravets, Jay Johnson, Howard Lin,
Elaine Tan, Don Wang

 NEST Family Entertainment™

Level One

 NEST Family Entertainment™

Parent and Teacher Guide

Studies have proven learning is enhanced through the use of several senses. A recent study shows that we retain 10 percent of what we see, 20 percent of what we hear, and 50 percent of what we see and hear. But when we see, hear and do, we retain 90 percent of the information.
(*Lisa Marie Nelson, Ph.D., Author "The Healthy Family Handbook"*).

The purpose of this Resource & Activity Book is to help children learn and retain the story theme and principles in a fun and educational way. Your children will love coloring pages, solving puzzles, matching games, completing word searches, and much more! Each Resource & Activity Book also features challenging questions and activities for children from preschool through middle school. And in the rare case you don't know an answer, there's an answer key in the back.

LEVEL OF DIFFICULTY

The activities in this book are designed in three levels of difficulty and segregated into two challenging sections. The Level One section of the book contains activities geared towards younger children while the Level Two section contains activities that are more challenging. Each activity also includes a symbol designating the difficulty level of that activity. The activities with one symbol are easy for most children while the two and three symbol activities become increasingly challenging for older children.

Level One
Easy

Level Two
Intermediate

Level Three
Advanced

TABLE of CONTENTS

" Peter is arrested. "
Acts 12:14

Jesus sent an angel to rescue Peter from prison. Isn't it great to know that Jesus loves us?

Color J blue   Color L purple

Color E red   Color O orange

Color S green   Color V brown

Color U yellow   Color M pink

I love him, too.

" **The Guards search for Jason.** "

Word Puzzle

Find and circle all of the words in the puzzle below.
The words are listed below the puzzle.
The first one has been done for you.

P	R	A	Y	A
E	X	R	U	N
T	W	T	N	G
E	L	O	V	E
R	C	E	L	L

✓cell   pray   angel   Peter   love   run

" Jason tells of Peter's arrest. "

Shape Match-Up

Read the sentences below. Each sentence has a missing word inside a shape. Find the matching shape in the word box below and you will find the missing word. Write the word in the blanks to complete the sentence.

1. **Peter was a**  .

2. **An**  **came to Peter.**

3. **The Lord's** _ _ _ _ _ _ .

4. **Thine is the** _ _ _ _ _ _ _ .

5. **Peter was set**  .

WORD BOX

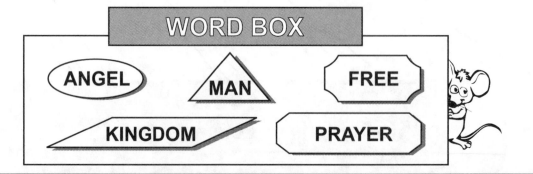

ANGEL   MAN   FREE

KINGDOM   PRAYER

" Jason sneaks into the prison."

Find the Word

What must we do to find an answer? To find out, color all the X's red, all the Y's blue, and all the Z's green.

Z	Z	X	S	Y
Y	X	Z	Z	Z
E	Y	Y	X	Z
X	X	E	Y	Z
Z	Y	Z	X	K

Copy all the letters that are not colored on the blanks below. Copy them in order from the top.

___ ___ ___ ___

and you shall find. Matthew 7:7

"The Roman Captain reads the charge to Peter."

"The Christians learn that Peter
is charged with treason."

Maze for the Answer

What fell from Peter through the power of prayer?
Go through the maze to find the answer.

glasses   patch   chains

"Mary reminds everyone
to pray."

Matching Scrolls

In Peter's day, letters were written on scrolls. There are five scrolls below. Color the two that match.

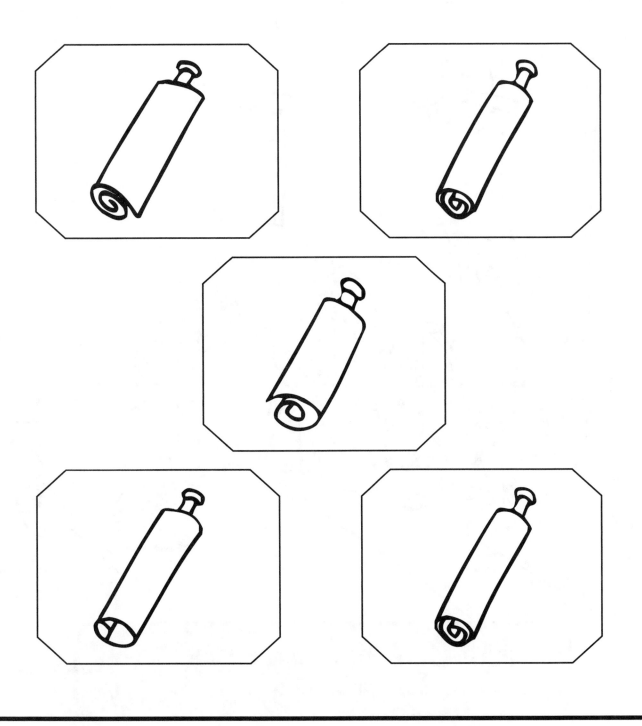

"The Christians pray for Peter."
Acts 12:5

Color the Shapes

Color the shapes with four sides to find a hidden word. The letters spell a word that shows how Jesus helped others by their faith. Unscramble the colored letters and copy them on the blanks below.

___ ___ ___ ___ ___

"The man in need."
Luke 11:5-8

"The Parable of the Judge."
Luke 18:1-5

Find the Words

Follow each step below to find what happened to Peter after the Christians prayed.

Step 1: In the line below, cross out all the As.

A A H A E A A

Write the letters that are left in the blanks below.

___ ___

Step 2: In the line below, cross out all the Bs.

B W B B A S B

Write the letters that are left in the blanks below.

___ ___ ___

Step 3: In the line below, cross out all the Cs.

F C R C E C E C

Write the letters that are left in the blanks below.

___ ___ ___ ___

Read all the words together to find what happened to Peter.

"**Joash tries to bribe the guards.**"

Level Two

 NEST Family Entertainment™

TABLE of CONTENTS

Math Madness

Find the sums below to discover what Jesus told us to pray. Your answers will give you the code letters to write on the blanks.

1 + 2 = ___ T		3 + 3 = ___ H
3 + 1 = ___ Y		1 + 0 = ___ L
1 + 1 = ___ B		6 + 1 = ___ E
4 + 1 = ___ D		4 + 4 = ___ W
8 + 2 = ___ O		5 + 4 = ___ N
		6 + 5 = ___ I

"

___ ___ ___
3   6   4

___ ___ ___ ___
8   11   1   1

___ ___   ___ ___ ___ ___
2   7   5   10   9   7
"

(Matthew 6:10)

RATING

¿? Mystery Word ?¿

There is one thing that is very important when we are praying for others. Follow the steps below to find what this is.

STEP ONE: Read the list of words below. If the word belongs to the story, circle the letter in the YES column. If the word does not belong, circle the letter in the NO column.

	YES	NO
1. Roman Guard	P	A
2. Noah	E	O
3. Peter	S	B
4. Sugar Cane	R	S
5. Camels	T	I
6. Prison	B	S
7. Prayer	L	K
8. Jesus	E	L

STEP TWO: Write all of the circled letters in order on the blanks to complete the sentence.

"All things are

___ ___ ___ ___ ___ ___ ___ ___

to those who believe." Mark 9:23

BACK-WORDS

Jesus taught His disciples how to pray. Work the puzzle below to find out how He wanted them to begin.

Step One: If the sentence is true, circle the backwards word in the TRUE column. If it is false, circle the word in the FALSE column.

	TRUE	FALSE
1. Peter was placed under arrest.	ruo	yht
2. Peter was charged with treason.	rehtaF	sa
3. Peter had very little faith.	it	hcihw
4. Peter was visited by a man.	dael	tra
5. The guards tricked Joash.	ni	su
6. Jesus prayed in the garden of Gethsemane.	nevaeH	dna

Step Two: Copy the words you circled onto the blank spaces in Row One. Then write each word spelled forward in Row Two.

Row One ___ ___ ___ ___ ___ ___

Row Two ___ ___ ___ ___ ___ ___ .

+MATH MATCH-UPS-

Solve the puzzle to find what the angel said to Peter.

Step One: Match the math question on the left with the answer on the right. Use a ruler to draw a straight line. Every line will cross one letter in the Letter Column.

MATH EQUATIONS	LETTER COLUMN	MATH ANSWERS
3 + 1 = ●	G	● 9
	R	
9 - 2 = ●	A	● 2
	N	
5 + 4 = ●	O	● 10
	D	
6 - 3 = ●	F	● 4
	O	
4 - 2 = ●	N	● 5
	L	
7 + 3 = ●	L	● 7
	D	
1 + 5 = ●	E	● 3
	L	
4 - 3 = ●	O	● 8
	W	
6 + 2 = ●	M	● 6
	X	
7 - 2 = ●	T	● 1

Step Two: Finish the angel's statement below by filling in the missing letters. Starting at the top of the Letter Column, copy the letters that your lines went through in order, in the blanks.

"Put on your sandals and your

cloak ___ ___ ___   ___ ___ ___ ___ ___ ___   ___ e."

Acts 12:8

RATING

"Joash is tricked."

FILL the BLANK

Use the words in the box below to complete this scripture verse.

Lord	cell	chains	hands	light
appeared	Peter's	up	him	angel

And Behold, an _____ of the _____ suddenly _____, and a _____ shone in the _____; and he struck _____ side and roused _____, saying, "Get _____ quickly." And his _____ fell off his _____ .

Acts 12:7

RATING

SUPER Proofreader

The story below contains ten misspelled words. Become a "Super Proofreader" by circling the misspelled words and then spelling the words correctly on the lines below the story.

And He went a lettle beyond thim, and fell on His face and prayed, seying, "My Father, ef it is possable, lut thes cup paz from Me; yet nat as I will, but az Thou wilt."

Matthew 26:39

RATING

" Peter follows the angel. "
Acts 12:8

When Peter was freed from prison, he went to Mary's house. What did Peter tell the believers?

Use the code below to fill in the blanks and discover what Jesus did.

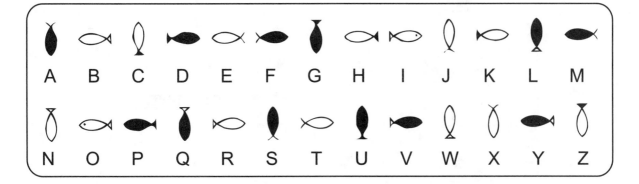

| A | B | C | D | E | F | G | H | I | J | K | L | M |
| N | O | P | Q | R | S | T | U | V | W | X | Y | Z |

Peter stopped the believers from coming to him

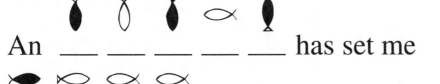

and he said, "I ___ ___ ___ ___ the

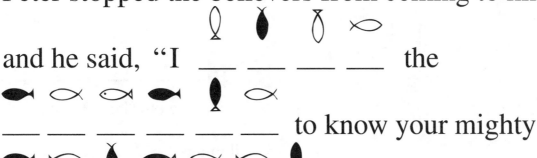

___ ___ ___ ___ ___ ___ ___ ___ to know your mighty

___ ___ ___ ___ ___ ___ ___ ___ have been heard.

An ___ ___ ___ ___ ___ has set me

___ ___ ___ ___ ___ !" Acts 12:16-17

TM & ® NEST, ©2005 Nest Masters II, Inc. May be reproduced for non-commercial, personal or classroom use per Permission to Reproduce guidelines. All other rights reserved. NEST Family Entertainment™ ▪ 1461 S. Beltline Rd., Ste 500 ▪ Coppell, TX 75019

Crossword Puzzle

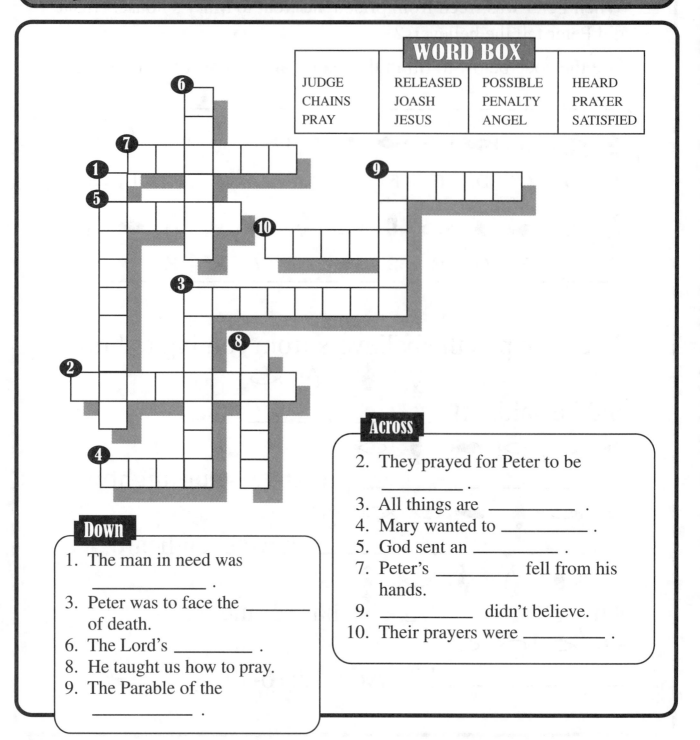

Across

2. They prayed for Peter to be _____ .
3. All things are _____ .
4. Mary wanted to _____ .
5. God sent an _____ .
7. Peter's _____ fell from his hands.
9. _____ didn't believe.
10. Their prayers were _____ .

Down

1. The man in need was _____ .
3. Peter was to face the _____ of death.
6. The Lord's _____ .
8. He taught us how to pray.
9. The Parable of the _____ .

RATING

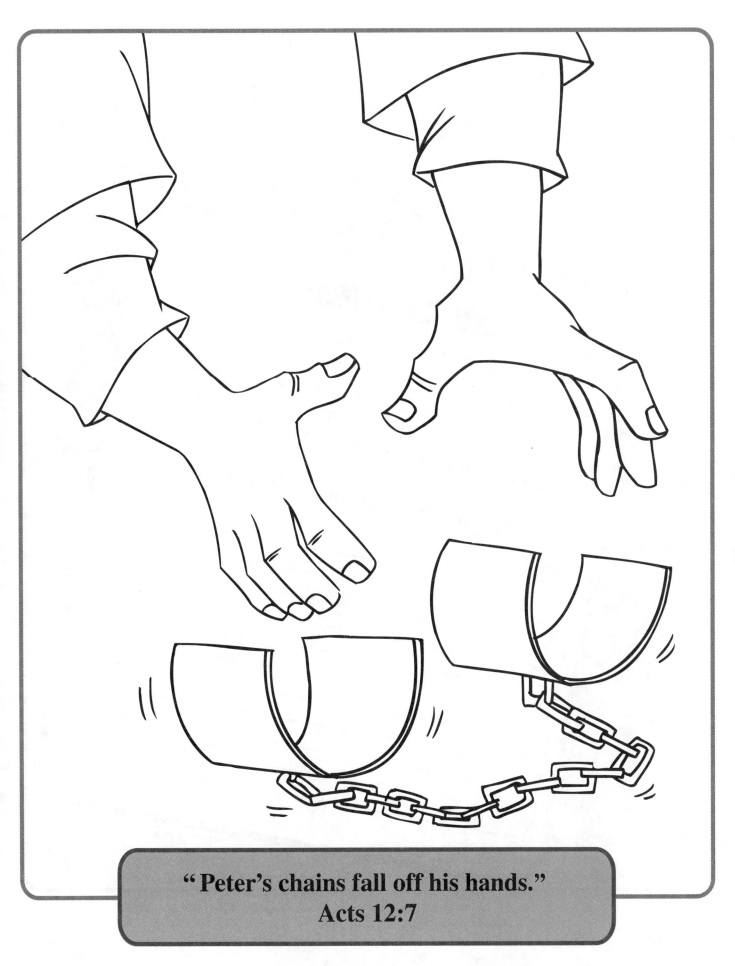

"Peter's chains fall off his hands."
Acts 12:7

JESUS & ME

The Christians gathered together to pray for Peter's freedom. Pretend you are one of the believers gathered at Mary's home; how do you think you would have prayed?

Write your thoughts on the lines below.

_____

_____

_____

_____

_____

_____

_____

_____

RATING

WORD CIRCLE

What can we receive daily? You can find out by using the word wheel below. Begin at the "5" and follow the arrows (clockwise) circling each number that is a multiple of five. Then go around the wheel again, and write down the letters matching the circled numbers on the blanks below.

" —— —— —— —— ——   —— ——   —— —— —— ——

—— —— —— ——   —— —— ——

—— —— —— —— —— ——   —— —— —— —— —— —— . "

Acts 6:11

RATING

"Peter comforts Joash."

Number each of the following sentences in the order that they happened in the story. Then follow the directions below to check your answers.

_____ **E**veryone was praying while Rhoda went to answer the door.

_____ **N**ow that Peter was arrested, Mary asked everyone to pray.

_____ **A**fter Peter was arrested, Jason ran from the guards.

_____ **L**et's remember that the power of prayer set Peter free.

_____ **G**iven the charge of treason, Peter would face the penalty of death.

In numbered order, place the first letter of each sentence in the blanks below. If you numbered correctly, the letters will spell who came to Peter's cell.

_____ _____ _____ _____ _____

RATING

MULTIPLICATION

If you solve these multiplication challenges, you will be able to solve the mystery at the bottom of the page. Cross out each number in the answer box as it is used, then circle all the unused answers. The word under the unused answers will solve the mystery!

4 x 11 = ____   2 x 8 = ____   10 x 8 = ____   4 x 5 = ____

7 x 5 = ____   9 x 5 = ____   6 x 6 = ____   10 x 9 = ____

                     3 x 5 = ____   6 x 2 = ____

A N S W E R B O X			
12 WAY	90 DO	16 HEAL	15 DESTROY
5 AND	35 BE	36 LORD	44 ANGEL
20 HELP	80 BOY	18 SEEK	45 FORTH

Solve the Mystery!

"Ask, and it shall be given to you;

_____ , _____ ye shall find."

Matthew 7:7a

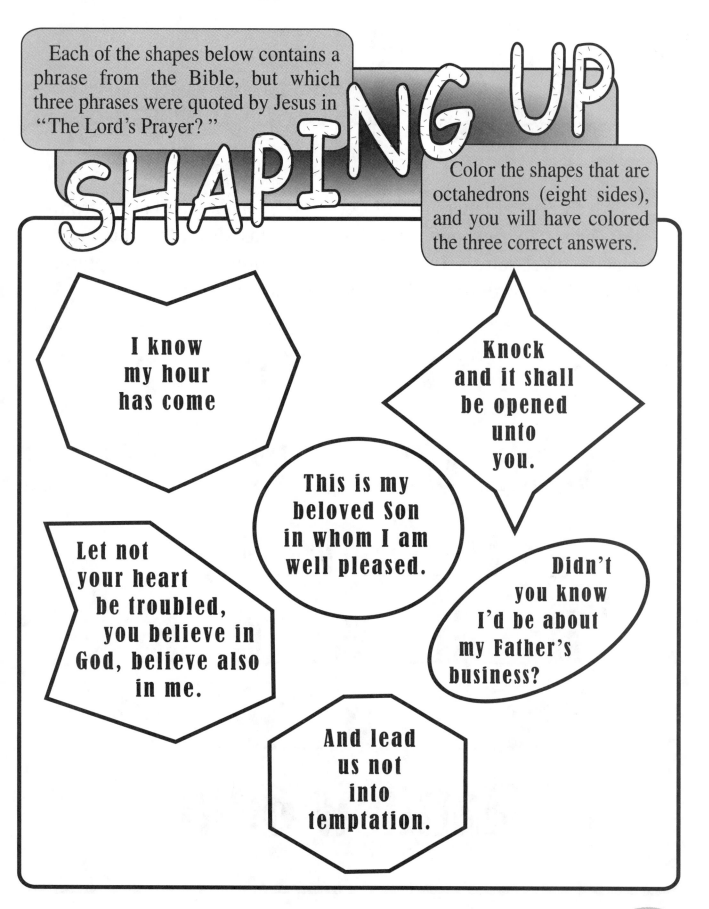

SHAPING UP

Each of the shapes below contains a phrase from the Bible, but which three phrases were quoted by Jesus in "The Lord's Prayer?"

Color the shapes that are octahedrons (eight sides), and you will have colored the three correct answers.

I know my hour has come

Knock and it shall be opened unto you.

This is my beloved Son in whom I am well pleased.

Let not your heart be troubled, you believe in God, believe also in me.

Didn't you know I'd be about my Father's business?

And lead us not into temptation.

RATING

All the vowel letters (A,E,I,O,U, and Y) have faded away from this page. To find out what Jesus told his disciples you must place vowel letters in the blanks to complete the scripture. (Hint: One word uses a "Y" as a vowel letter.)

" __ __ r F__ th__ r
wh__ ch __ rt __ n
h __ __ v__ n,
H __ ll __ w __ d b__ __
th__ __ n __ m__ ."

Matthew 6:9b

SOUNDS RIGHT

Homonyms are words that sound alike, but have different meanings. A sample of a pair of homonyms is "die" and "dye."

Look for the pairs of homonyms in the blocks below. When you find a pair, color the entire block. When you finish, you will discover the answer to the riddle below.

Question: **How many soldiers guarded Peter?**

bow bough	love dove	one won	neigh nay	pair pare
hey hay	nice niece	bye buy	sample simple	ache lake
whale wail	doze daze	mourn morn	so sew	reign rain
gnu new	hop hope	way weigh	cane can	tee tea
hair hare	heal seal	know no	our hour	ore or

RATING

"Peter stops the believers."
Acts 12:17

TRUE or FALSE

Read the statements below. If it is true, circle the "T." If it is false, circle the "F."

1	Jesus said that all things are possible.	T	F
2	Peter was charged with stealing.	T	F
3	Peter was a disciple of Jesus.	T	F
4	Give us this day our daily bread.	T	F
5	The entire country prayed for Peter.	T	F
6	Jesus prayed in the garden of Bethlehem.	T	F
7	Jesus knew His hour had come.	T	F
8	An Angel came to Peter.	T	F
9	The guards were amazed by the angel.	T	F
10	Rhoda was the first to see Peter at the gate.	T	F

Take an *S.A.T.
*Scripture Awareness Test

1) Who was the King at the time of Peter's arrest? (Acts 12:1-4)

_____

2) Who gathered together and prayed for Peter? (Acts 12:5)

_____

3) Where did the Roman guards take Peter? (Acts 12:4)

_____

4) What was the charge against Peter?

_____

5) In The Lord's Prayer, whom are we to forgive? (Matthew 6:12)

_____

6) In The Lord's Prayer, what are we to be delivered from? (Matthew 6:13)

_____

7) What should we do to have our prayers answered? (Matthew 7:7)

_____

8) What will a friend do in a time of need? (Luke 11:8)

_____

9) What important thing did the widow do in the parable of the unjust judge? (Luke 18:4-5)

_____

10) Was Jesus ever sad? (Matthew 26:38)   Do you know why?

_____

11) What command had Jesus given Peter? (John 21:16)

_____

12) What opened by itself to Peter and the angel? (Acts 12:10)

_____

RATING

THE LORD'S PRAYER

POINTS TO PONDER

1. **M**aybe you know the Lord's prayer by heart. What is your favorite passage?

2. **D**o you think that Christians should pray everyday? Why?

3. **P**retend that you are Peter and that you have been thrown into prison for no crime but being a Christian. Do you think Jesus would hear your prayers?

4. **W**hy do you think Rhoda ran back into the house to tell the others about Peter without stopping and talking to him?

RATING

ANSWER KEY
LEVEL ONE

WORD PUZZLE — PAGE 8

P	R	A	A	Y	A
E	X	R	U	N	N
T	W	T	N	G	G
E	L	O	V	E	E
R	C	E	L	L	L

SHAPE MATCH-UP — PAGE 10

1. MAN
2. ANGEL
3. PRAYER
4. KINGDOM
5. FREE

FIND THE WORD — PAGE 12

Z	Z	X	**S**	Y
Y	X	Z	Z	Z
E	Y	Y	X	Z
X	X	**E**	Y	Z
Z	Y	Z	X	**K**

Answer: SEEK

ANSWER KEY
LEVEL ONE

MAZE FOR THE ANSWER — PAGE 15

glasses   patch   chains

COLOR THE SHAPES — PAGE 19

M

R   Y

S   P   A

P   R   A   Y

MATCHING SCROLLS — PAGE 17

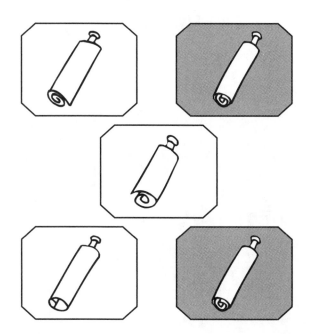

FIND THE WORDS — PAGE 22

H E

W A S

F R E E

MATH MADNESS – PAGE 29

1 + 2 =	*3*	T		3 + 3 =	*6*	H
3 + 1 =	*4*	Y		1 + 0 =	*1*	L
1 + 1 =	*2*	B		6 + 1 =	*7*	E
4 + 1 =	*5*	D		4 + 4 =	*8*	W
8 + 2 =	*10*	O		5 + 4 =	*9*	N
				6 + 5 =	*11*	I

$$\frac{T}{3} \quad \frac{H}{6} \quad \frac{Y}{4}$$

$$\frac{W}{8} \quad \frac{I}{11} \quad \frac{L}{1} \quad \frac{L}{1}$$

$$\frac{B}{2} \quad \frac{E}{7} \qquad \frac{D}{5} \quad \frac{O}{10} \quad \frac{N}{9} \quad \frac{E}{7}$$

(Matthew 6:10)

MYSTERY WORD – PAGE 30

Answer: POSSIBLE

BACK WORDS – PAGE 31

Row One	*ruo*	*rehtaF*	*hcihw*	*tra*	*ni*	*nevaeH*
Row Two	*our*	*Father*	*which*	*art*	*in*	*Heaven*

MATH MATCH-UPS – PAGE 32

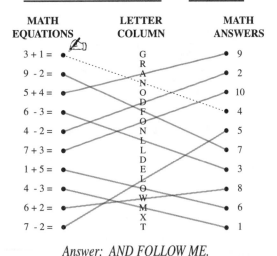

MATH EQUATIONS	LETTER COLUMN	MATH ANSWERS
3 + 1 =	G R A N O D F O N L L D E L O W M X T	9
9 - 2 =		2
5 + 4 =		10
6 - 3 =		4
4 - 2 =		5
7 + 3 =		7
1 + 5 =		3
4 - 3 =		8
6 + 2 =		6
7 - 2 =		1

Answer: AND FOLLOW ME.

FILL THE BLANK – PAGE 34

angel	*light*	*him*
lord	*cell*	*up*
appeared	*Peter's*	*chains*
		hands

SUPER PROOFREADER – PAGE 35

Misspelled words = Correct spelling

lettle	=	*little*		*lut*	=	*let*
thim	=	*them*		*thes*	=	*this*
seying	=	*saying*		*paz*	=	*pass*
ef	=	*if*		*nat*	=	*not*
possable	=	*possible*		*az*	=	*as*

PICTURE CODE – PAGE 37

Answer: want, people, prayers, angel, free

CROSSWORD – PAGE 38

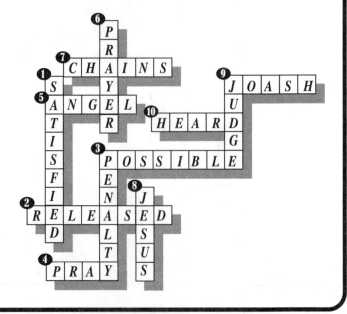

ANSWER KEY
LEVEL TWO

WORD CIRCLE — PAGE 41

Answer: " GIVE US THIS DAY OUR DAILY BREAD."

FIRST THINGS FIRST — PAGE 43

Answer: 4, 2, 1, 5, 3
ANGEL

MULTIPLICATION MYSTERY — PAGE 44

4 x 11 = __44__   2 x 8 = __16__   10 x 3 = __30__   4 x 5 = __20__
7 x 5 = __35__   9 x 5 = __45__   6 x 6 = __36__   10 x 9 = __90__
3 x 5 = __15__   6 x 2 = __12__

ANSWER BOX			
12 WAY	90 DO	16 HEAL	15 DESTROY
5 AND	35 BE	36 LORD	44 ANGEL
20 HELP	80 BOY	18 SEEK	45 FORTH

Answer: SEEK, AND

SHAPING UP — PAGE 45

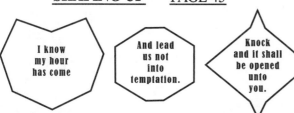

VANISHING VOWELS — PAGE 46

Answer: "OUR FATHER WHICH ART IN HEAVEN HALLOWED BE THY NAME."
MATTHEW 6:96

SOUNDS RIGHT — PAGE 47

bow bough	love dove	one won	neigh nay	pair pare
hey hay	nice niece	bye buy	sample simple	ache lake
whale wail	doze daze	mourn morn	so sew	reign rain
gnu new	hop hope	way weigh	cane can	tee tea
hair hare	heal seal	know no	our hour	ore or

Answer: 16

TRUE OR FALSE — PAGE 49

1. T   3. T   5. F   7. T   9. F
2. F   4. T   6. F   8. T   10. T

TAKE AN S.A.T. — PAGE 50

1) *King Herod*
2) *The Church*
3) *Prison*
4) *Treason*
5) *Our debtors*
6) *Evil*
7) *Ask, seek, knock*
8) *He will still give him everything he needs.*
9) *She didn't give up.*
10) *Yes. Soon He would be crucified.*
11) *Feed my sheep.*
12) *The gate that lead to the city.*

SCRIPTURE REFERENCES

Peter is arrested
The arrest .... Acts 12:4

The Church prays for Peter
Prays without ceasing .... Acts 12:5

Ask, seek, knock
Ask and it shall be given .... Matthew 7:7

Luke 11:9

For everyone that asks .... Matthew 7:8

Luke 11:10

The Friend in need
Lend me some bread .... Luke 11:5-8

The Parable of the Unjust Judge
We should always pray .... Luke 18:1

The Parable .... Luke 18:2-5

Jesus explains the Parable .... Luke 18:6-8

Jesus instructs Peter
Feed my sheep .... John 21:16

SCRIPTURE REFERENCES

The Lord's Prayer

Pray humbly .... Matthew 6:6

God knows all things .... Matthew 6:8

" Our Father which art in heaven, Hallowed be Thy name" .... Matthew 6:9

" Thy kingdom come, Thy will be done, on earth as it is in heaven." .... Matthew 6:10

" Give us this day our daily bread" .... Matthew 6:11

" And forgive us our debts, as we forgive our debtors" .... Matthew 6:12

" And lead us not into temptation, but deliver us from evil: For thine is the
    kingdom, and the power and the glory forever. Amen." .... Matthew 6:13

NOTES

SCRIPTURE REFERENCES

Peter in Prison and the Angel

Peter between two guards .... Acts 12:6

Behold the angel .... Acts 12:7

Peter's chains fall .... Acts 12:7

Put on your sandals .... Acts 12:8

Peter followed the angel .... Acts 12:9

The city gate .... Acts 12:10

The angel leaves .... Acts 12:10

Peter knows the Lord had rescued him .... Acts 12:11

Peter goes to Mary's home

The Christians are gathered in prayer .... Acts 12:12

Peter knocks on the gate .... Acts 12:13

Rhoda came to the gate .... Acts 12:13-14

Rhoda runs back to the others .... Acts 12:14

The Christians didn't believe Rhoda .... Acts 12:15

Peter stops the people .... Acts 12:17

Certificate of Achievement

This certifies that

has mastered the

The Lord's Prayer

RESOURCE & ACTIVITY BOOK

LEVEL ONE

from NEST Family Entertainment™

by successfully completing all of the puzzles, games, and activities found herein.

NEST Family Entertainment

As of this date

Certificate of Achievement

This certifies that

_____

has mastered the

The Lord's Prayer

RESOURCE & ACTIVITY BOOK

LEVEL TWO

from NEST Family Entertainment™

by successfully completing all of the puzzles, games, and activities found herein.

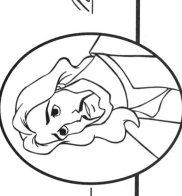

NEST Family Entertainment

_____

As of this date